What Else Can I Play?

Alto Saxophon

Grade Four

Series Editor: Miranda Steel

Music arranged and processed by
Barnes Music Engraving Ltd
East Sussex TN22 4HA, England

Cover design by Headline Publicity

Published 2000

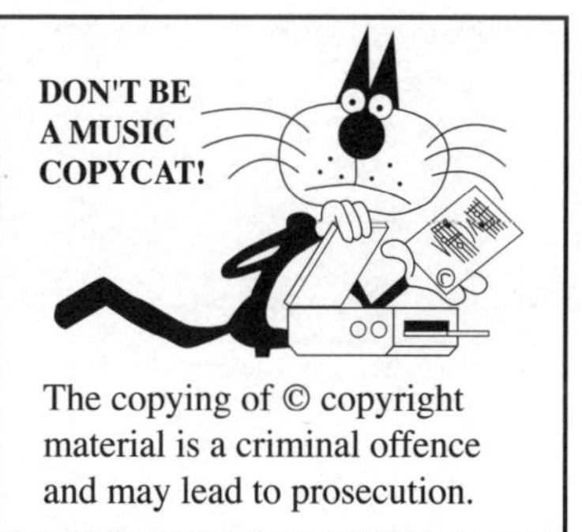

Introduction

In this *What Else Can I Play?* collection you'll find eighteen popular tunes that are both challenging and entertaining.

The pieces have been carefully selected and arranged to create ideal supplementary material for young saxophonists who are either working towards or have recently taken a Grade Four saxophone examination.

As the student progresses through the volume, technical demands increase and new concepts are introduced which reflect the requirements of the major examination boards. Suggestions and guidelines on tempo and dynamics are given for each piece, together with technical tips and performance notes.

Pupils will experience a wide variety of music, ranging from classical and jazz through to showtunes and popular songs, leading to a greater awareness of musical styles.

Whether it's for light relief from examination preparation, or to reinforce the understanding of new concepts, this collection will enthuse and encourage all young saxophonists.

Daydream believer

Words and Music by John Stewart

Moderately fast, with a swing (♩ = 120)

Alto Saxophone

Piano

mf

4

mf

8

12

16
21
26
30
34

38
42
46
f
f
51
55
mf
rit.
p

Try to remember

Music by Harvey Schmidt

Slow waltz (♩ = 116)
Alto Saxophone
Piano
mp legato
5
mp
10
mf
mf
16

21
f
f
26
mp
mp
31
36
rit.

Close to you (they long to be)

Music by Burt Bacharach

20
3
24
mf
Ped.
29
mf
33

It's alright with me

Words and Music by Cole Porter

19
2.
mp
24
29
35
mf
mf

41
46
50
55
f
f
ff
ff

Coronation Street

Music by Eric Spear

Moderately slow (♩ = 88)
Alto Saxophone
Piano
mp
mp
3

4
3

7
3

10
13
16
mf
mf
con Ped.
20
rit.

a tempo
mp
mp
rubato
rit.
f

Singin' in the rain

Music by Nacio Herb Brown

What Else Can I Play?
Alto Saxophone
Grade Four

Daydream believer

Words and Music by John Stewart

'Daydream Believer' became a top ten hit for The Monkees in 1967. The band was conceived as a television show about a struggling pop group, and were more of a popular than critical success, especially when it was discovered that they did not play on their early records. Carole King, Neil Diamond and Harry Nilsson all wrote for them at different times.

Play this melody with lots of expression, but keep it fairly light. Pay particular attention to the dynamics, especially the *crescendos* and *diminuendos* on the long tied notes.

Try to remember

Music by Harvey Schmidt

This is perhaps the best known song from *The Fantasticks*, one of the longest running American stage musicals. It opened on the 3rd of May 1960 and ran for over 12,000 performances. The song has been recorded by the actor Edward Woodward, among others.

Look at the overall shape of this piece – see how the melancholy melody gradually grows to its peak around bar 21, and then gently calms down towards the end. Pay attention to the dynamics, especially the *diminuendo* in the last three bars.

Close to you (they long to be)

Music by Burt Bacharach

'Close To You' was the first hit for the brother-and-sister duo, the Carpenters. It was written by Burt Bacharach and Hal David, one of the most successful musical partnerships in the history of popular music.

This piece should sound very relaxed and not forced. Note that the dotted rhythms should be played in a 'swing' style. Count the beats for the longer notes correctly so that they are not cut short.

It's alright with me

Words and Music by Cole Porter

Despite interrupting his career to join the French Foreign Legion during the First World War, Cole Porter's talent as a jobbing songwriter foreshadowed his later success. 'It's Alright With Me' from his smash hit musical 'Can Can' has been recorded by over forty different artists, from Harry Connick Jnr. to the Zombies.

Count the value of the tied notes carefully, especially at bars 19–20 and 27–28; don't rush the quaver runs that follow. Breath at the end of each phrase to keep the music moving along.

Coronation Street

Music by Eric Spear

Coronation Street was first shown at 7pm on the 9th of December 1960 and is the longest running TV show in the United Kingdom. A number of famous names have cropped up on the programme, including Joan Collins, Davy Jones (later of The Monkees) and Martin Shaw (Doyle from *The Professionals*).

This is a tune that we have all heard at some time or other. A slightly lazy style would be good; make the most of the triplets and don't make the dotted notes too snappy. A couple of tricky fingerings in this piece will be helped by slow practice.

Singin' in the rain

Music by Nacio Herb Brown

Although 'Singin' In The Rain' is best remembered as the title song of the 1952 film, it had been used in two earlier films, *Hollywood Revue* and *Little Nelly Kelly*. In addition to songwriting, Arthur Freed was an important producer of film musicals for the MGM studio, and revived it for Gene Kelly's memorable dance number.

Keep this piece light and bouncy, almost dance-like. Take care with the syncopated rhythm at bar 34 – use the last crotchet in the bar as an anchor point. Bars 37 to 40 may need a bit of practice; especially if you are to get the dynamics and change in tempo correct.

Talk to the animals

Words and Music by Leslie Bricusse

Leslie Bricusse wrote both the script and song score for the film of *Dr. Dolittle* in 1967. It was revived as a West End musical over thirty years on with Philip Schofield in the lead role. Bricusse collaborated with Anthony Newley (who was in the film) on a number of projects, and together they wrote the words to the title song of the James Bond movie *Goldfinger*.

This is a playful melody in three sections. The first is similar to the third and the middle section (from bar 13) creates a contrast. This middle section will need some careful attention as it is both high and *legato*, apart from the accented notes in bars 20 and 21.

Music to watch girls by

Words and Music by Anthony Verona and Sid Ramin

First made popular by Andy Williams in the 60s, 'Music To Watch Girls By' was revived more recently for a car advertisement on television. In 1945, Williams dubbed Lauren Becall's singing voice in her first film with Humphrey Bogart, *To Have And Have Not*.

You can give the melody a bit of a lift by playing the notes very slightly short. Pay attention to the rhythm, giving some of the syncopated notes a bit of an accent.

Love's got a hold on my heart

Words and Music by Andrew Frampton and Pete Waterman

This was a hit for the pop quintet Steps. Pete Waterman, who co-wrote it, firmly established himself as a writer/producer in the 80s with Matt Aitken and Mike Stock as Stock, Aitken and Waterman. The trio modelled themselves on the Motown hit factory of the 60s.

This is a melody that needs to be played with lots of feeling. Some of the rhythms are not easy and it might help to try counting in quavers when you first practise this piece.

The greatest love of all

Music by Michael Masser

This song was written as part of the soundtrack for a 1977 film called *The Greatest* which was about the life of Muhammad Ali, who played himself. In the film it was sung by George Benson, but has since been recorded by Whitney Houston.

The melody line of this piece is taken from the vocal line and is fairly syncopated throughout. Despite the complexity of the rhythms, it is important that it should be played with lots of expression.

April in Paris

Music by Vernon Duke

Vernon Duke is best known for his musical and film scores, although he also developed a style for choral works, operas, ballets and chamber works. This piece became known for accompanying the famous scene in the 1953 film, where Doris Day and Ray Bolger dance in the street after their romantic day is interrupted by wind and rain.

Evenly space all the triplet crotchets and try to play them *legato* and in a relaxed manner. There are *fermatas* in bar 28; make these notes slightly longer than their actual value.

The Pink Panther theme

Music by Henry Mancini

This was the title music of the 1964 film starring Peter Sellers. Henry Mancini, who wrote it, was a pianist and arranger with the Glenn Miller orchestra. He wrote a lot of film music, including the song 'Moon River' from *Breakfast at Tiffany's* (1961), for which he won an Oscar.

This piece should be played with a very 'mysterious' feel. Pay attention to the dynamics, especially in the last 5 bars; notice how each bar is quieter than the previous one – until the last *sforzando* (suddenly loud) note.

Star Wars (main title)

Music by John Williams

Son of a studio musician, John Williams became a multi-instrumentalist as a boy and broke into film work early in his career. He has been prolific, earning more than twenty-five Oscar nominations. He scored Ronald Reagan's last film, *The Killers* in 1964.

This is a march with a very striking tune that should be played very majestically. Keep the triplets nice and crisp and make the most of the big finish. Feel the force!

Toreador's song

Music by Georges Bizet

'Toreador's Song' is taken from *Carmen* by Georges Bizet, which was his last theatrical work of note. When it was first staged in 1875 the audience was indifferent and the press was scandalised by the unapologetic caprices of the heroine.

This piece is a proper march. Everything should be bang on: rhythm, tempo, staccati. The dotted rhythms should be quite snappy and the triplets should be crisp. And don't forget the dynamics!

I got rhythm

Music and Lyrics by George Gershwin and Ira Gershwin

'I Got Rhythm' is from the Broadway show *Girl Crazy* (1932). It marked Ethel Merman's rise from nightclub singer to Broadway star. She was in a supporting role and it was the only song she had, but she made her presence felt, holding a high C for 16 bars in the coda. Never a retiring character, Cole Porter described her as being like a "brass band going by".

As the title would suggest, rhythm has a particularly important part to play in this piece! To begin with, play it slowly with a metronome: you'll learn all the rhythms much more quickly that way.

In the mood

Music by Joe Garland

Although it is most widely remembered as an instrumental piece popularised by Joe Loss and particularly Glenn Miller, 'In The Mood' was written in 1939 by Joe Garland, a saxophonist and arranger for dance and jazz bands. The original version had lyrics and was a success in its own right.

The quavers should be played in a swing style, as indicated at the beginning. Make sure that you observe all the accents – they are really important to the 'feel' of the piece. There are some tricky phrases in this piece which will require slow practice. Playing your chromatic scales and arpeggios will help.

Mexican hat dance

Traditional

This is a piece of traditional Mexican dance music. The first performance on record was at the Coliseo in Mexico City in 1790. It appeared more recently in the 1945 film *Anchors Aweigh* starring Frank Sinatra and Gene Kelly.

This piece has a compound time signature, so remember that each beat divides into three. Don't be late at the start of the phrases – always aim for the first beat of the bar.

In the hall of the mountain king

Music by Grieg

'In The Hall Of The Mountain King' is part of the *Peer Gynt Suite,* which was commissioned by Henrik Ibsen as incidental music to his play *Peer Gynt*. The musical suite was first published as a piano duet.

This piece is not easy! You've got a lot to think about – the articulation (the staccato and accents are great tonguing practice!), the accidentals – and it's fast as well! Practise the piece slowly at first, until you are comfortable with all the fingering.

Reproduced and printed by
Halstan & Co. Ltd., Amersham, Bucks., England

2/00

You can be the featured soloist with

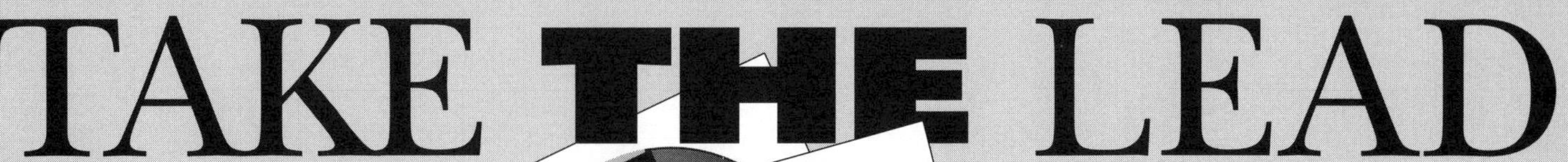

clarinet
Now you can be the feature clarinet soloist on eight specially recorded arrangements
TAKE THE LEAD
clarinet
FEATURES
Full backings to play along with
Full demonstration tracks to help you learn the songs
Carefully selected and edited arrangements
Chord symbols in concert pitch
TAKE THE LEAD
MOVIE HITS
clarinet disc
MOVIE HITS

Collect these titles, each with demonstration and full backing tracks on CD.

90s Hits

The Air That I Breathe (Simply Red)
Angels (Robbie Williams)
How Do I Live (LeAnn Rimes)
I Don't Want To Miss A Thing (Aerosmith)
I'll Be There For You (The Rembrandts)
My Heart Will Go On (Celine Dion)
Something About The Way You Look Tonight (Elton John)
Frozen (Madonna)

Order ref: 6725A – Flute
Order ref: 6726A – Clarinet
Order ref: 6727A – Alto Saxophone
Order ref: 6728A – Violin

Movie Hits

Because You Loved Me (Up Close And Personal)
Blue Monday (The Wedding Singer)
(Everything I Do) I Do It For You (Robin Hood: Prince Of Thieves)
I Don't Want To Miss A Thing (Armageddon)
I Will Always Love You (The Bodyguard)
Star Wars (Main Title) (Star Wars)
The Wind Beneath My Wings (Beaches)
You Can Leave Your Hat On (The Full Monty)

Order ref: 6908A – Flute
Order ref: 6909A – Clarinet
Order ref: 6910A – Alto Saxophone
Order ref: 6911A –Tenor Saxophone
Order ref: 6912A – Violin

TV Themes

Coronation Street
I'll Be There For You (theme from *Friends*)
Match Of The Day
(Meet) The Flintstones
Men Behaving Badly
Peak Practice
The Simpsons
The X-Files

Order ref: 7003A – Flute
Order ref: 7004A – Clarinet
Order ref: 7005A – Alto Saxophone
Order ref: 7006A – Violin

Christmas Songs

The Christmas Song (Chestnuts Roasting On An Open Fire)
Frosty The Snowman
Have Yourself A Merry Little Christmas
Little Donkey
Rudolph The Red-Nosed Reindeer
Santa Claus Is Comin' To Town
Sleigh Ride
Winter Wonderland

Order ref: 7022A – Flute
Order ref: 7023A – Clarinet
Order ref: 7024A – Alto Saxophone
Order ref: 7025A – Violin
Order ref: 7026A – Piano
Order ref: 7027A – Drums

The Blues Brothers

She Caught The Katy And Left Me A Mule To Ride
Gimme Some Lovin'
Shake A Tail Feather
Everybody Needs Somebody To Love
The Old Landmark
Think
Minnie The Moocher
Sweet Home Chicago

Order ref: 7079A - Flute
Order ref: 7080A - Clarinet
Order ref: 7081A - Alto Saxophone
Order ref: 7082A - Tenor Saxophone
Order ref: 7083A - Trumpet
Order ref: 7084A - Violin

21
27
33
p
38
rit.
pp
pp

Talk to the animals

Words and Music by Leslie Bricusse

17
21
mf
mf
26
cresc.
cresc.
30
ff
ff

Music to watch girls by

Words and Music by Anthony Verona and Sid Ramin

17
21
f
f
26
mf
mf sub.
30
34

Love's got a hold on my heart

Words and Music by Andrew Frampton and Pete Waterman

16
20
mp cresc.
mp cresc.
23
27
f
f

31
35
p
p
40
f
f
44
molto rit.
ff
ff

The greatest love of all

Music by Michael Masser

Slowly, with feeling (♩ = 70)
rit.
Alto Saxophone
Piano
p
a tempo
4
p
7
3
11
mf
mf

© 1977 & 2000 EMI Gold Horizon Music Corp and EMI Golden Torch Music Corp, USA
Worldwide print rights controlled by Warner Bros Publications Inc/IMP Ltd

14
18
rit.
a tempo
22
f
27

31
36
p
p
41
f
45
rit.
pp
p
pp

April in Paris

Music by Vernon Duke

Moderately (♩ = 96)
rit.
Alto Saxophone
Piano
p
a tempo
mf
f

21
f
f
25
rit.
p
p
29
a tempo
3
mf
mf
33
f
f
37
rit.
slower
mp
mp
pp
p
pp
Ped.

The Pink Panther theme

Music by Henry Mancini

13
16
f
19
mf
mp
mp
p
22
p
sfz
sfz

Star Wars (main title)

Music by John Williams

rubato

Toreador's song

Music by Georges Bizet

Moderate march (♩ = 118)

13
f
f
17
21
mf
3
25

I got rhythm

Music and Lyrics by George Gershwin and Ira Gershwin

20
25
f
mf
f
mp
30
35
f
f

39
mf
mf
44
49
54
ff
ff

In the mood

Music by Joe Garland

Fast swing (♩ = 152) (♫ = ♩³♪)
Alto Saxophone
Piano
f
f
5
9
13

17
21
25
29

33
36
39
42
ff
ff

Mexican hat dance

Traditional

Very fast (♩. = 126)
Alto Saxophone
Piano
mf
f
5
10
15

20
mf
mf
25
f
29
f
34
ff
ff

In the hall of the mountain king

Music by Grieg

Fast march (♩ = 138)
Alto Saxophone
Piano
f
pp
pp sub.
5
9
13

17
21
mp
mp
25
29
mf
mf

Reproduced and printed by
Halstan & Co. Ltd., Amersham, Bucks., England

Why not extend your repertoire with:

Congratulations! You've Just Passed Grade 1

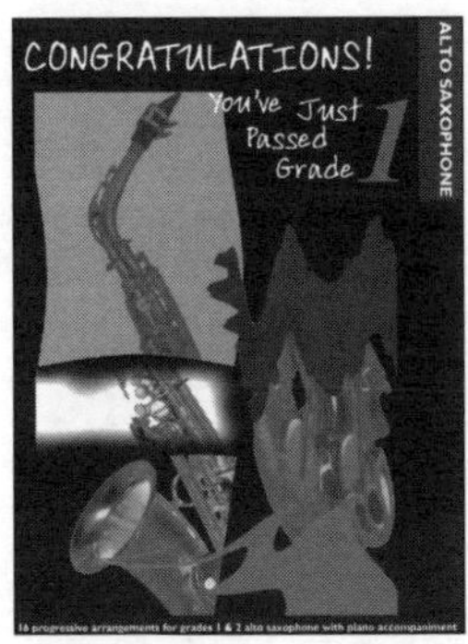

6796A
Alto Saxophone

6797A
Clarinet

6794A
Flute

6798A
Piano

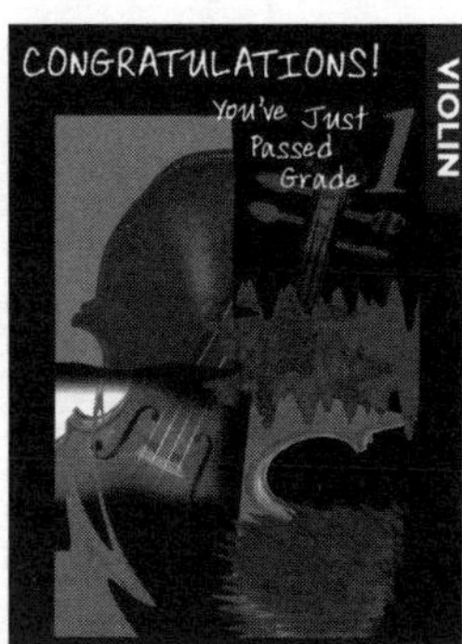

6795A
Violin

- Features standard repertoire which is ideal for Grades 1-2.
- Available for clarinet, alto saxophone, flute and violin with piano accompaniment; and piano solo.
- A wide variety of titles from jazz to pop, and from classical to folk.
- Fifteen great progressive titles in each book.

Series includes: *Angels – Autumn Leaves – Blueberry Hill – Bye Bye Blackbird – Don't Bring Lu Lu – The Hippopotamus Song – How Do I Live – I Don't Want To Miss A Thing – I'm Forever Blowing Bubbles – I've Got No Strings – Jeepers Creepers – My Heart Will Go On*